SINGER EDITION 5-PAK

Santa goes green

HOLIDAY MUSICAL
FOR YOUNG VOICES

*by John Jacobson
and Mac Huff*

W9-BSC-363

TABLE OF CONTENTS

Musical Performance Rights

HAL•LEONARD®
CORPORATION
7777 W. BLUEMOUND RD. P.O. BOX 13819 MILWAUKEE, WI 53213

Visit Hal Leonard Online at
www.halleonard.com

1. Merry Merry Christmas

Words and Music by JOHN JACOBSO
and MAC HUF
Arranged by MAC HUF

Bright and Happy (♩ = 155)

23 *mf*
Mer - ry, Mer - ry Christ - mas___ ev - 'ry-one__ is here.___

Snow - men danc - ing mer - ri - ly,___ spread - ing Christ - mas cheer.

31
___ San - ta's hap - py help - ers___ are

load - ing up__ the sleigh.__ Ev - 'ry - thing__ is read

- y___ for a mer - ry Christ-mas day.__ We're sing - in'

40
Mer - ry Christ - mas, sing__ Mer-ry Christ-mas, Mer - ry Christ - mas great
Mer - ry Christ - mas, sing__ Mer-ry Christ-mas, Mer - ry Christ - mas ev-

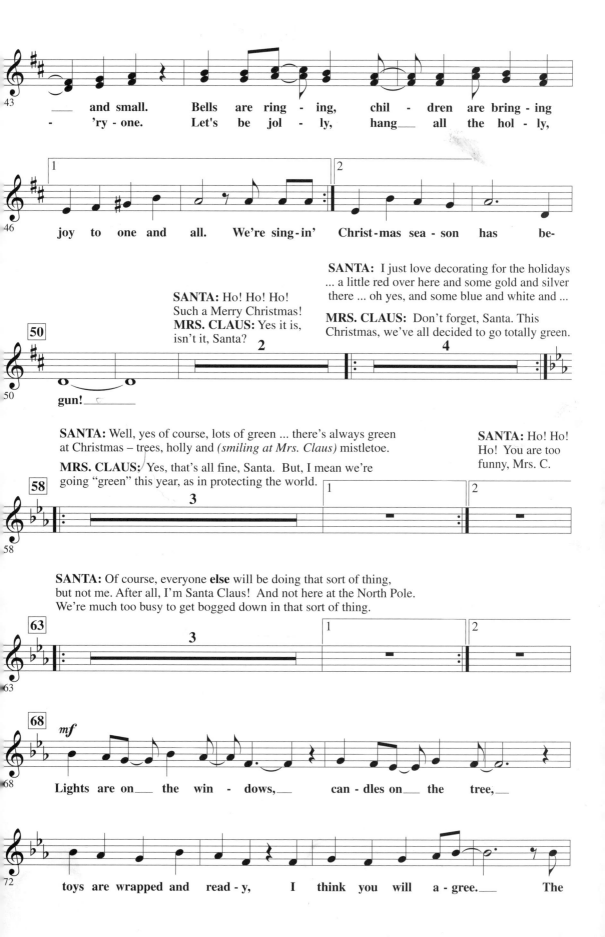

_____ and small. Bells are ring - ing, chil - dren are bring - ing
- 'ry - one. Let's be jol - ly, hang____ all the hol - ly,

joy to one and all. We're sing-in' Christ-mas sea - son has be-

SANTA: I just love decorating for the holidays ... a little red over here and some gold and silver there ... oh yes, and some blue and white and ...

MRS. CLAUS: Don't forget, Santa. This Christmas, we've all decided to go totally green.

SANTA: Ho! Ho! Ho! Such a Merry Christmas!
MRS. CLAUS: Yes it is, isn't it, Santa?

gun!____

SANTA: Well, yes of course, lots of green ... there's always green at Christmas – trees, holly and *(smiling at Mrs. Claus)* mistletoe.

MRS. CLAUS: Yes, that's all fine, Santa. But, I mean we're going "green" this year, as in protecting the world.

SANTA: Ho! Ho! Ho! You are too funny, Mrs. C.

SANTA: Of course, everyone **else** will be doing that sort of thing, but not me. After all, I'm Santa Claus! And not here at the North Pole. We're much too busy to get bogged down in that sort of thing.

mf

Lights are on____ the win - dows,____ can - dles on____ the tree,____

toys are wrapped and read - y, I think you will a - gree.____ The

76 rein-deer are ex - cit - ed and read - y to take flight.

80 Ev - 'ry-thing is read - y for this ver - y spe - cial night.

f > > > **85**

We're sing - in' Mer-ry Christ - mas, sing Mer-ry Christ-mas,
Mer - ry Christ - mas, sing Mer - ry Christ-mas,

Mer - ry Christ - mas great and small. Bells are ring - ing, chil-
Mer - ry Christ - mas ev - 'ry - one. Let's be jol - ly, hang

1
- dren are bring - ing joy to one and all. We're sing - in'
all the hol - ly,

2
Christ - mas sea - son has be - gun!

Mer - ry Christ - mas ev - 'ry - one!

STOP RECORDING

Scene 1
Elves enter carrying solar panels.

Elf 1:	Merry Christmas, Mr. and Mrs. Claus.
Mrs. Claus:	Merry Christmas, Elfies.
Elf 2:	Now, where would you like these solar panels, Mrs. C?
Santa:	Solar panels?
Mrs. Claus:	Oh, up on the housetop ought to do it, fellas.
Elves 1 and 2:	You got it. Click, click, click!

Rudolph enters.

Mrs. Claus:	Oh hi, Rudolph. All ready for the big night?
Rudolph:	*(talking like a slow drawling cowpoke)* Howdy, Mrs. C. I reckon I'm 'bout ready now. How do ya'll like my new "Smart" nose? Lasts ten times longer than the old one and uses up a fraction of the power.
Mrs. Claus:	*(rubbing his nose)* It looks as bright and shiny as ever, Rudolph.
Santa:	*(alarmed)* Solar panels? Smart noses? What's going on here?
Mrs. Claus:	Santa dear, it's time you get with the program. It may seem inconvenient at times, but we're all going "green" this year and you might as well get green too.
Santa:	*(to the audience)* Green?
Mrs. Claus:	That's right. Green – as in environmentally-friendly. Green – as in ever … green. Green – as in … well, sing it, Sequoia!

START RECORDING

Song 2: The Greenhouse Effect

2. The Greenhouse Effect

Words and Music by JOHN JACOBSON
and MAC HUFF
Arranged by MAC HUFF

you.   I saw San-ta's rein-deer surf-ing off the North Pole Pier!

you.   The

And

elves are spread-ing Cop-per-tone® in - stead of Christ-mas cheer.   And

do   we   have   to   men - tion   that   it's   real - ly   hot   in   here?

do   we   have   to   men - tion   that   it's   real - ly   hot   in   here?

Yes,   we   sus - pect   the   Green-house   Ef - fect!

Yes,   we   sus - pect   the   Green-house   Ef - fect!

STOP RECORDING

Scene 2

Santa: The Greenhouse Effect? Melting ice caps? No wonder my neighbors seem to be getting closer every year.

Elf 3: So you see, Santa, we're all working together to try to save the planet by making Christmas ever more green this year.

Santa: But … but …

Evergreen Tree 1: Ever green. I like the sound of that.

Santa: More green?

Evergreen Tree 2: You can never have too much green for my tastes, if you know what I mean?

(Trees give each other a "high five.")

Elf 2: We've got to change soon or we're going to come up short. Get it … short?

Santa: You mean, I have to give up everything that I like, like TV and Christmas lights, heat in my workshop and gas in my sleigh?

Rudolph: No! No! No! We don't mean that at all. Now listen ya'll, I've got a nose for this kind of thing. I happen to know that there are actually some things y'all can do that don't have to make our lives less comfortable, but can actually help save the world.

Mrs. Claus: Really, Rudolph? Like what?

Rudolph: *(smiling)* So glad you asked. Hit it, fellers.

START RECORDING

Song 3: Turn Off the Pump

3. Turn Off the Pump
(and Plug in the Sleigh)

Words and Music by JOHN JACOBSON
and MAC HUFF
Arranged by MAC HUFF

43

Part I

Turn off the pump and plug in the sleigh.

Part II

mp

I yi yi yi._____ Get a-

It's gon - na be a green hol - i - day. We're

long, lit - tle rein - deer._____

pow - ered up now and we're read - y for flight. So,

I yi yi yi._____ So,

(All)   *mf* **59**

please don't for - get to turn off the lights. The night is up-

on us and we're rea - dy to go. The moon's high a-

bove us, the earth far be - low. With San - ta in

tow, up the chim - ney we rose, and Ru - dolph out

now and we're read-y for flight. So, please don't for-

102 yi yi yi._____ So, please don't for-

get to turn off the lights. So please

106 get to turn off the lights. So please

dim. *rit.*

turn off the lights._____

dim. *rit.*

110 turn off the lights._____

STOP RECORDING

Scene 3

Rudolph: Quick, plug it in one more time to give us a little more juice before take off.

Dasher: Okay! Here goes!

12 *Sound Effect (Plugs in the sleigh and there is a blackout except for Rudolph's nose.)*

Dasher: Oops!

(Lights come back on.)

Santa: Turning off the lights, oh dear! It just won't seem like Christmas without all of the twinkling lights on the rooftops and evergreen trees.

Toy Soldier 1: Oh, Santa. It doesn't mean you can't have any lights.

Toy Soldier 2: That's right! It just means we have to get our energy in new and more efficient ways.

Mrs. Claus: *(dusting Rudolph's nose)* And cleaner too. *(Rudolph sneezes.)*

All: Bless you!

Toy Soldier 3: It's about power, Santa! New ways to get power to the people.

Santa: Power to the people?

All: Right on!

Santa: But wait! New noses? New power? I don't know if I like this idea. I like my old lights. I'm Santa Claus and I can't imagine giving up my SUS.

Elf 5: SUS?

Santa: Sport Utility Sleigh!

Evergreen Tree 1: Well, Santa, it isn't easy goin' green.

Evergreen Tree 2: But we've got to do our part or there won't be a world left for you to fly around on Christmas Eve.

Toy Soldier 4: It's not about giving up power, Santa. It's about developing new and better power that works great and doesn't ruin the world.

Elf 6: You see, Santa, it's not about giving up all the things we care about. It's about taking back what we love and protecting it.

Mrs. Claus: Power to the people! Oh, what a perfectly Christmassy idea! *(She gives a count off)* Uh one, Uh two, ah one, two, three four!

START RECORDING

Song 4: Power to the People!

4. Power to the People

Words and Music by JOHN JACOBSON
and MAC HUFF
Arranged by MAC HUFF

(start dialog on the repeat)
MRS. CLAUS: Come on, Rudolph, why don't you and
the rest of the reindeer rustle up some solar power?
RUDOLPH: Sure thing, Mrs. C.

be - cause__ we have to hoist up San - ta Claus!__

PENGUINS: *mp*

It's

MRS. CLAUS: *(to the elves)* Okay little fellers. How are we going to keep that sleigh flying and those bells ringing with the price of oil the way it is?

Pow - er to the peo-

so - lar, it's wind - y, it's wa - ter, that's pow - er! It's

ELF 1: Never fear, Mrs. C. You feel that breeze? That's pure energy!

- ple.

so - lar, it's wind - y, it's wa - ter, that's pow - er!

ELVES:
mf

Jin - gle bells, jin - gle bells, jin - gle all the way. Gon - na use a wind - mill to

pow - er up the sleigh, hey! Jin - gle bells, jin - gle bells, jin - gle all the way. The

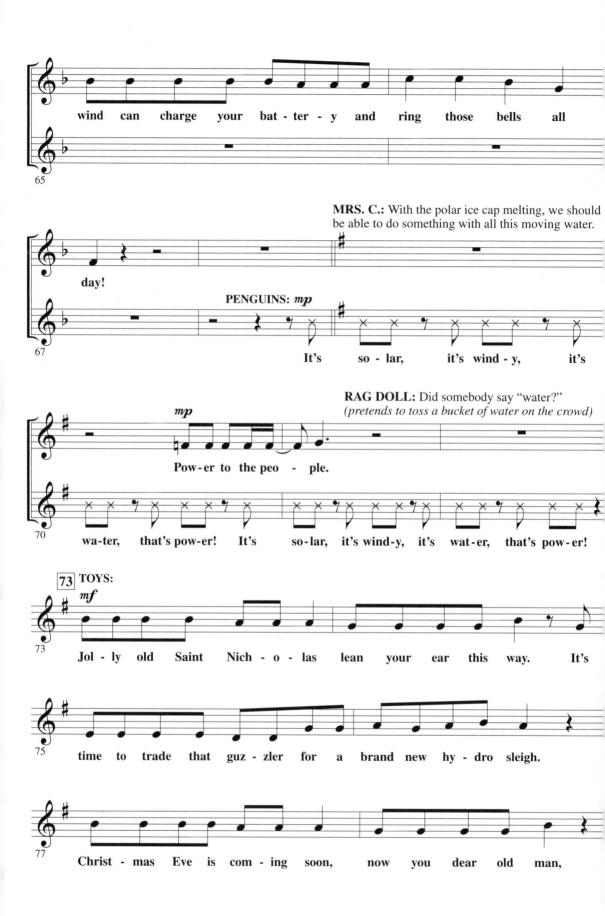

wind can charge your bat - ter - y and ring those bells all

day!

MRS. C.: With the polar ice cap melting, we should be able to do something with all this moving water.

PENGUINS: *mp*

It's so - lar, it's wind - y, it's

mp

Pow - er to the peo - ple.

RAG DOLL: Did somebody say "water?"
(pretends to toss a bucket of water on the crowd)

wa - ter, that's pow - er! It's so - lar, it's wind-y, it's wat - er, that's pow - er!

73 **TOYS:**

mf

Jol - ly old Saint Nich - o - las lean your ear this way. It's

time to trade that guz - zler for a brand new hy - dro sleigh.

Christ - mas Eve is com - ing soon, now you dear old man,

get your wa - ter pow - er from the Her - bert Hoov - er Dam. The

Herb - ert Hoov - er Dam! Oh!

Pow - er to the peo - ple; We can find a way...

Pow - er to the peo - ple; Each and ev - 'ry day.

Pow - er to the peo - ple; That means you and me...

Pow - er to the peo - ple; it will set___ you

free, set you free!

Pow - er to the peo - ple, yeah, yeah, yeah!___

We've got the pow - er!

STOP RECORDING

Scene 4

Santa: Well, I guess I could use a battery-powered sleigh, if you reindeer wouldn't be offended.

Vixen: Are you kidding? A little back-up power sounds like a great idea!

Elf 5: That's a good start. But we're going to have to do more than that, if we're going to save this holiday.

Elf 6: Not to mention this planet!

Snowman:
Caroline We've got to get used to more recycling, instead of throwing everything away we *think* we've used up.

Mrs. Claus: What do you mean, Snowman.

Snowman:
Caroline Well, take this old silk hat I'm wearing. I've been considering trading it in for a newer model. But now that I think about how full our landfills are getting, I think I'll just keep wearing it until it completely falls apart. Then I'll recycle it and use it as something else, like a shopping bag or a cool bowtie.

Mrs. Claus: Oh, I get it. By using less, re-using what we have and recycling all that we can, we can help cure the things that are ruining our planet.

Comet: Bingo! Mrs. C. Reduce, Re-use, Recycle. That's the key to saving the world!

Santa: Reduce, Re-use, Recycle. Reduce, Re-use, Recycle. Ho Ho Ho! I like the sound of that. *(pause)* But how does it work?

Baker Elf:
Grace It's easy, Santa! Take this fruitcake, for instance. We've been re-cycling it for years!

Santa: Ho Ho Ho! ... Really?

START RECORDING

Song 5: Recycle the Fruitcake

5. Recycle the Fruitcake

Words and Music by JOHN JACOBSON
and MAC HUFF
Arranged by MAC HUFF

Grand - ma has a fruit - cake, it's been in store for years. So
fruit - cake can be wide, a fruit - cake can be thin. A

ev - 'ry year at Christ - mas time it mag - ic - 'lly ap - pears. She
fruit - cake can be tox - ic so they keep it in a tin. So

got it free in fif - ty three at Ma - cy's or at Sears.
when you get a fruit - cake, nev - er let it touch your skin,

When it goes back to the at - tic, no one sheds a tear. Re-
'cause you nev - er real - ly know where fruit - cakes might have been. }

cy - cle the fruit - cake, re - cy - cle the fruit - cake.

Send it to a cou - sin or an un - cle and then, where-

ev - er   you take it,   you   won't   have   to   fake   it,   'cause

ev - 'ry-bod - y   knows   a   fruit - cake   comes   a - round   a-

gain   and   a - gain   and   a - gain,   a - gain,   a - gain.   (HEY!)

(2nd time only)

2 **SANTA:** Oh, I get it. If we recycle, we can save the world!!

A

MRS. CLAUS: Recycling will certainly help, Santa dear. But there are many more things we can do as well.

repeat as needed

ALL: LIKE WHAT!?

MRS. CLAUS: **SOLO 2:**

Ride   a   bike   or   take   a   hike.   Re - cy - cle all   your   mail.   A-

(whale sound)

void   fast food   or   may - be   you'd   a - dopt   a   hump - back   whale.

SOLO 4:   **SOLO 6:**

Ad - vo - cate   or   in - su - late,   ac - cu - mu - late   less   stuff.   A

com-post pile makes a rein-deer smile, that ought to be e-

SANTA: *(optional spoken)*

MRS. CLAUS: Oh, no dear.
(then shouts) *f*   CAST: *f*   MRS. C.:   CAST: MRS. C.:

nough.   Give me an R!   R! Give me an E!   E! Give me a

ALL:

C - Y - C - L - E   RE - CY - CLE!   Re-

cy - cle   the fruit - cake,   re - cy - cle   the fruit - cake.

Send   it   to   a   cou - sin   or   an   un - cle   and then,   where-

ev - er   you take it,   you   won't   have   to   fake   it,   'cause

ev - 'ry-bod - y   knows   a   fruit - cake   comes a - round a - gain.   'Cause

ev - 'ry-bod - y   knows   a   fruit - cake   comes a - round a - gain and a - gain and a-

gain,   a - gain,   a - gain,   a - gain,   a - gain,   and a - gain!

STOP RECORDING

Scene 5

Santa: Okay, Okay! Ho Ho Ho! I think I get it! Recycling is about taking something and using it over and over again!

Elf 6: That's part of it, Santa. Recycling also means taking a product or material at the end of its useful life and turning it into a usable raw material to make another product.

Elf 7: Like aluminum cans. They can be used, recycled and back on the shelf in something like 60 days!

Grace

Toy Soldier 1: Even Christmas trees can be recycled.

Santa: Really? Christmas trees?

Toy Soldier 1: *(relishing it)* Sure. We can chop them into tiny bits to be used for compost or mulch.

Toy Soldier 2: *(very upbeat)* Chopped, smashed and ground to bits, these trees contain valuable nutrients that can help the Earth!

Evergreen Tree 1: I think I'm going to be sick.

Rudolph: Ya see Santa, global warming is real. The greenhouse effect **is** happening. But we're not helpless to do something about it, are we, ya'll?

Snowman: That's right, Rudolph. There are lots of things that we can do to reverse the trend and save the world.

Caroline

Mrs. Claus: It's our world after all. And Christmas is a great time to change our ways and treat the world like the precious gift it is.

Santa: *(in awe)* Ho Ho Ho! It's our world! It truly is. It truly is.

START RECORDING

Song 6: It's Our World

6. It's Our World

Words and Music by JOHN JACOBSON
and MAC HUFF
Arranged by MAC HUFF

STOP RECORDING
Scene 6

Santa: Ho Ho Ho! Well said, my friends! Well said.

Evergreen Tree 1:   You see, Santa, Christmas is the perfect time of year for all of us to turn over a new leaf …

Evergreen Tree 2:   Or needle…and start treating our world a whole lot better.

Santa: Now I know exactly what you mean! From now on, Christmas at the North Pole is going to be red and blue …

Snowman: Covered in white!

Mrs. Claus: Silver and gold!

Santa: And especially …

All: Green!!!

START RECORDING
Song 7: We're Goin' Green

7. We're Goin' Green

Words and Music by JOHN JACOBSON
and MAC HUFF
Arranged by MAC HUFF